NICK JR. The BACKYARDIGANS
Music Player
Storybook™

written by Christine Ricci
illustrated by Jason Fruchter
based on the original teleplays by
Janice Burgess (Princess CleoTasha) and McPaul Smith (Pirate Treasure)

Contents

Reader's Digest Children's Books®

Pleasantville, New York • Montréal, Québec • Bath, United Kingdom

Pirate Treasure

Play Song 1 "Arrr!" said Uniqua as she looked through her telescope. "I'm Captain Uniqua, the patch-eyed pirate! You can tell I'm a pirate because I say, 'Arrr!'"

"Arrr!" replied Captain Austin. "I'm a pirate too—a pirate with a hook for a hand!" Suddenly, Captain Uniqua saw something in the sandbox. It was half of a pirate treasure map!

"Only half of a map?" asked Captain Austin. "Too bad we don't have the whole map."

"Half of a map is better than nothing!" said Captain Uniqua. "Come on, matey! Let's go find the treasure." Captains Uniqua and Austin climbed aboard their pirate ship and sailed off on their quest for pirate treasure.

Play Song 2

Soon after, Tyrone and Pablo walked over to the sandbox. As they dug in the sand, Pablo's shovel uncovered half of a pirate treasure map.

"Too bad it's not the whole map," said Tyrone.

"But half a map is better than nothing," replied Pablo. "Let's be pirates and look for the treasure! I'll be Captain Pablo. Arrr!"

"I'll be Captain Tyrone," said Tyrone. "Arrr!" Captains Tyrone and Pablo took their half of the treasure map, climbed aboard their pirate ship, and set sail for the high seas!

Captains Pablo and Tyrone spotted the other pirate ship in the distance. They quietly sailed their boat next to the ship and secretly climbed aboard. "Arrr! We're raiding your ship, you scurvy pirates," said Captain Pablo.

"Arrr! Well, we're defending our ship, you scurvy pirates!" Captain Austin returned. "Arrr!"

"Arrr!" The pirates said, "Arrr!" at each other as they tried to raid and defend the ship.

"Arrrrr! We win!" cheered Captain Tyrone. "And that means that Captains Uniqua and Austin have to walk to the end of the plank and splash into the water!"

"Hey! That sounds like fun," said Captain Pablo. "Maybe WE should walk the plank."

"Uh-uh," said Captain Uniqua. "YOU won the raid, so WE get to walk the plank."

Play
Song
3
Captains Uniqua and Austin climbed up on the plank, and walked forward until they got to the very end. Then they jumped. But instead of splashing into the water, they landed in the soft, warm sand of a desert island—a desert island just like the map said they needed to find. Excited, the pirates ran down the beach in search of treasure.

"Come on, matey," Captain Pablo said to Captain Tyrone as they jumped out of the boat. "We can use our half of the map to find the treasure!"

After walking for a long time without finding any treasure, Captains Pablo and Tyrone stopped to check their half of the map. Captains Austin and Uniqua were studying their own half of the map when they bumped right into the other pirates. The two maps went flying and landed side by side on the desert sand, making one map. In the middle of this map, an X marked the spot where the treasure was buried. Knowing that they needed both halves of the map to find the treasure, the pirates agreed to work together to look for the X.

Play
Song
4

The first mark they came to was a T. Then they came to a U, and a V, and finally a W.

"No one would bury treasure under a T, U, , or W," said Captain Uniqua.

"Yeah, only X marks the spot," said Captain yrone. "Let's keep looking!"

The next mark they came to was the X.

"All right, mateys! Let's dig for treasure!" xclaimed Captain Austin.

Each of the pirates grabbed a shovel and began o dig. Before long, Captain Uniqua's shovel hit omething in the sand. It was the treasure chest!

Play Song 5

Inside the treasure chest was the biggest and most beautiful diamond in the entire world.

"We're rich!" exclaimed Captain Tyrone.

But Captain Pablo was worried. "What if other pirates try to raid us to capture our diamond? Maybe we should hide our treasure."

The pirates thought Captain Pablo might be right. After all, pirates are known for raids. They decided to bury the treasure again. But as soon as the treasure was buried, Captain Pablo started to pace back and forth across the sand. "Oh, no! I've forgotten where we buried it. Where is the treasure?"

"We buried it right here," said Captain Tyrone, pointing at the sand.

Play
Song
6

"Oh yeah," said Captain Pablo. "Maybe we should mark the spot so we won't forget where it is."

"We could use an X to mark the spot," suggested Captain Uniqua.

But somehow using an X didn't seem quite right since all pirates used X to mark the spot. The pirates wanted to be trickier. They wanted to mark their spot with something that no one would ever think to look under. The pirates thought … and thought … and thought. All of a sudden, it came to them. They marked their treasure spot with a Y. What a pirate-y adventure!" exclaimed the pirate friends as they set sail for home.

Princess CleoTasha

Play Song 1

Once upon a time there was a princess. "I'm not just any princess. I am Princess CleoTasha from ancient Egypt," said the princess. "Where are my servants?" Servants Austin, Tyrone, and Pablo ran up to Princess CleoTasha and bowed. "Here we are, your highness."

The servants were always fulfilling the princess' demands. When she was hot, they fanned her. When she was hungry, they brought her sandwiches. When she was thirsty, they brought her water. Unfortunately, the princess never said, "please" or "thank you."

Play Song 2

One day, the princess wanted to be taken to her palace on the banks of the deep, green, River Nile. But when they arrived, it was hot and dusty, the garden was wilted, and the River Nile was dry land. Princess CleoTasha was very unhappy.

"Fill up the river!" she ordered.

"Only you can fill the river with water," replied Servant Tyrone. "You need to learn the secret of the Nile." The servants told Princess CleoTasha that if she brought three very special presents to Sphinx Uniqua, the Sphinx would reveal the secret. Reluctantly, Princess CleoTasha agreed to find the presents and visit Sphinx Uniqua.

First, they had to find the Jewel of the Waters. They weren't on the road very long when Princess CleoTasha became hot. "Let's stop here! I need to be fanned."

Servant Tyrone waved a large fan up and down to give the princess air. The fan was quite heavy and Servant Tyrone was so tired from the journey that he leaned against a wall— an invisible wall with a secret door that opened to reveal hundreds of sparkling jewels!

"Wow, look at all these incredible jewels!" the princess said. She wanted to keep all the jewels for herself, but she could only take the Jewel of the Waters. Otherwise, she wouldn't be told the secret of the Nile. "Find me the jewel," she ordered. Servant Tyrone pointed it out to her.

"I found the Jewel of the Waters!" Princess CleoTasha declared. "It's heavy! You carry it." She tossed the jewel to her loyal servant.

Servants Pablo and Austin asked if Servant Tyrone had helped the Princess find the jewel. "Yeah," nodded Servant Tyrone. "But you know Princess CleoTasha. She never says, 'please' or 'thank you.'"

Play Song 4

The second present was a yellow lotus flower from the top of the Cliffs of Karnak. The only way to the top was to walk up a very long flight of stairs. Princess CleoTasha hadn't climbed very many stairs when she grew tired and insisted that Servant Pablo carry her to the top. Of course, she did not say, "please." And when Servant Pablo got the princess to the top, she did not say, "thank you" either.

On the cliff top, the princess saw many beautiful flowers. She was about to pick some red and blue ones for herself when Servant Pablo reminded her that she could only pick one yellow flower as a gift to the Sphinx. "If you touch any other flower, you will not be told the secret."

"Oh, for goodness sakes," said the princess. "Where is this yellow flower?"

Servant Pablo helped Princess CleoTasha find the flower. "I have found the second present for the Sphinx!" she exclaimed, as she handed the flower to her servant.

"Princess CleoTasha never says, 'please' or 'thank you,'" Servant Pablo grumbled as he trudged down the stairs.

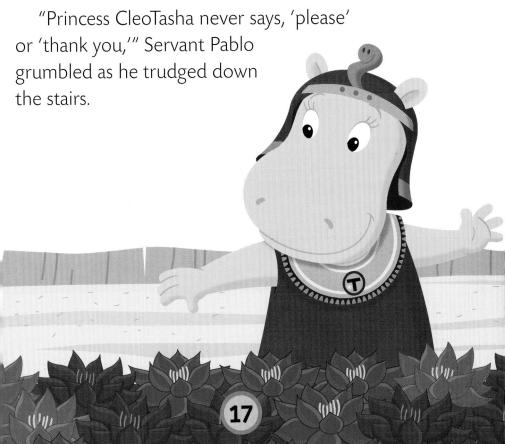

"What's the last present?" Princess CleoTasha asked.

Servant Austin told her it was water from the Secret Oasis. When they arrived at the oasis, they saw a crystal blue pool of water.

"Get out of my way," Princess CleoTasha yelled, as she ran toward the pool. "I'm so thirsty!"

"No, Princess!" Servant Austin shouted. "You cannot drink the water of the Secret Oasis! Only the Sphinx can drink it. You have to bring a cup of this water to the Sphinx."

Play Song 5

But none of the servants had a cup. "Well, how am I supposed to carry water without a cup?" complained Princess CleoTasha.

"You could use a curled leaf," suggested Servant Austin, and he handed her a leaf curled into a cup shape. Princess CleoTasha took it and filled it with water. "You carry it!" she muttered, as she handed it to Servant Austin. "Don't spill any!" And with that, she walked away.

Servant Austin turned to the other servants, "That Princess CleoTasha never says, 'please' or 'thank you.'"

"We know," they replied, as they gathered up the Sphinx's presents.

19

Play Song 6

"Greetings, O Sphinx Uniqua," Princess CleoTasha called out, as she and the servants approached the Sphinx. "I have brought you three presents so I can learn the secret that will fill the Nile River."

"I love presents," giggled Sphinx Uniqua. Princess CleoTasha gave her the three gifts.

"Very good," praised Sphinx Uniqua. "Getting these presents must have taken a lot of hard work," said Sphinx Uniqua. "Have you thanked your servants for all their help?"

"Well . . . no," the princess mumbled. Then the Sphinx leaned forward and whispered the secret of the Nile into Princess CleoTasha's ear.

"Oh, for goodness sakes," exclaimed the princess. Turning to her servants, the princess said, "Thank you for helping me find the gifts and for being such wonderful servants."

The servants were shocked. The princess had never, ever thanked them. Suddenly, they noticed that the Nile River was filling with water!

Then Sphinx Uniqua repeated the secret for everyone to hear. "The secret of the Nile—the secret to almost anything—is to always say 'please' and 'thank you.'"

"That reminds me, O Sphinx," Princess CleoTasha said. "Thank you for telling me the secret!" Then she turned to her servants. "Please come back to the palace and I'll get you a snack!" And they all happily returned to the palace.